*Published in July, 1992, by
The Wisconsin Department of
Agriculture, Trade and
Consumer Protection, Ag.
Resource Management
Division, Sustainable
Agriculture Demonstration
Program*

*This second edition is
dedicated to Wisconsin's
farmers, the finest, hardest
working and most vulnerable
people I have ever met.*

the author

FROM THE GROUND UP

• WISCONSIN •
SUSTAINABLE FARMERS
TELL OF THEIR
PRACTICE AND VISION

STORIES COLLECTED
AND EDITED BY

MIKE IRWIN

First edition 8,000 copies published July, 1990. Second edition 5,000 copies published July, 1992, ISBN 09633707-0-7.

Artwork and type for the first edition of this book originated with instructors and students at Madison Area Technical College. Illustrator John Ribble and production manager Robert Eason played a large role in the latest edition. DeGolier Publishing, Sun Prairie, Wisconsin is its printer. Funds for From the Ground Up, 1992, have been provided by money devoted to information delivery within the Sustainable Agriculture Demonstration Program.

Distributors of this edition include:

WDATCP Sustainable Agriculture Program
P.O. Box 8911
Madison, WI 53708-8911
Telephone orders: 608-273-6408

and

Wisconsin Rural Development Center
1406 Business Hwy. 18/151 East
Mount Horeb, WI 53572
Telephone orders: 608-437-5971

A Re-introduction

Forever, it seems, the Great Questions haunt, puzzle and dare us — and more people, and more, urban and rural — who produce and consume with conscience: Can we work the land, use the water and yet protect the sources? Preserve our children's inheritance and sustain ourselves? Can we farm and not live as slaves to capital or chemicals?

The men and women you'll meet here are pioneers in farm practice, yes, but they have also become teachers, writers, speakers. They meet groups from fellow and sister farmers to local Rotaries to Congressional committees. They've cast and have been cast by history into the Mainstream. And the Mainstream — if there is such a thing — has a bigger-than-ever stake in watching and hearing from them. They advise farm-related nonprofit organizations and university research teams. They're farmer demonstrators and some are DATCP's sustainable ag network leaders and members. As one sustainable producer put it: "We are partners in a maturing relationship, in a marriage you might say, between environmental safety and farm profit".

The Farmers Two Years Later

Rick Adamski plans an annual field day as a member of the Northeast Wisconsin Sustainable Farmers Network. He coaches farm visitors "at least three a week." These guests are interested in the carefully tuned, timed, fenced and watered systems, plant, animal, and technical ones, Adamski has become known for. Since 1990, he has created two permanent pastures, each with numerous day fences, and each of these "permanents" has a water delivery line and tank. Two years ago milk cows drank water at the barn morning and night and went to pasture between. Then, daily per-cow milk averages ran 45-55 lbs. Now, "letting them sip during the day," they're at 55-63 lbs. each. Adamski is moving toward seasonal milking. This means he'll plan artificial breeding of all cows within a single or two month cycle. Then, ceasing milking in November-December, he'll plan re-freshening of the herd through late winter and early spring.

Toni Christenson earns more of her organic market garden income from her Highway 57 *Bright Eye Farm* roadside store these days. She's kept a couple of supermarket accounts. But she notes, "deliveries have always been hard for me." In the 1992 cropping and marketing season, fully one-third of each section of the five acre raised bed garden is kept in a cover crop all or part of the year. Complete rotations, successions of crops within and across seasons, have been extended to ten years. She's become a Northeast farmers network member, and organic gardening columnist and a grain and vegetables cookbooks publisher.

Vince Hundt is a true believer in farm — and self-diversification. He has extended his entrepreneurial ways into sales of wood chipping, and paper shredding, baling and recycling equipment. He continues to buy, raise and sell replacement holstein heifers. He works in the woods harvesting sawlogs and firewood, clear-cutting small acreages and replanting red oaks, walnuts and pines. He serves as consultant to Wisconsin's plastic, and paper recycling industry.

Mike Irwin is planting and studying buckwheat, rye and annual or biennial clovers as cultural controls for weeds, and a number of host or "trap" crops for flea beetles which sometimes munch heavily on amaranth and azuki beans. He spreads alternate two-to-three acre fields with dolemite or calcite sources of calcium. "I'll watch these fields' tilth, weed populations, crop pest resistance and test plant tissues over ten years. I'm also exploring combination sources of complete plant proteins — no/low gluten proteins which are also high in calcium. Growing and milling these, we can meet the needs of many food allergy clients."

Bernie Kleiber has ridge-tilled cash crop corn and bean fields looking, to the uncritical eye, much like they did in 1990. Kliebers have continued using winter wheat frost-seeded with clovers in their rotation. But between wheat winterkills and nitrogen needs for the following corn crop, there lies a rub. Bernie's not sure right now if the wheat/legumes combo pencils out. "We are also thinking about drilling beans. Nancy would do it while I'm finishing up corn planting. Our goal would be to extend the bean season. We'd keep the same wheel traffic on the ridges but I'd build smaller ones to make combining possible." The "downside of the concept," he notes, is that he'd broadcast bean herbicide rather than banding it.

Ken Raspotnik has maintained a registered Polypay flock through lamb prices good and bad, but now also tends a three acre organic market garden and makes sales to Ashland stores and in open-air markets. Ken is coordinator of a 12-farmer network the DATCP Sustainable Ag. Demonstration Program has funded. The Chequamegon Organic Growers raise vegetables, potatoes, berries and apples. Raspotnik, network coordinator, has recently received a state ag department Agriculture Diversification and Development (ADD) grant. He is outfitting a commercial on-farm cannery. By fall 1992, salsas, fruit and berry sauces and jams, and vegetables bearing the *Organico* label will reach local and regional supermarkets. The Chequamegon Organic Growers will bring fresh products they didn't — or couldn't — direct market to the new plant.

Bob Schmidtknecht is more than ever the dairy farmer's farmer. Not long ago, a U.W. River Falls study confirmed what Bob has known for some time. His herd greatly outproduces and profits often double those of dairymen in his region who use tools, seed, field practices and dairy cow bloodlines similar to his. Is all the difference, or most of it, in the way one regards and treats the soil? Schmidtknecht thinks so. Also a member of the Western Wisconsin Farmers' network, he's received, independent of this membership, a new DATCP Sustainable Ag Demonstration grant to further document and teach what he's learned. Within a *biological farming* system, he's comparing and demonstrating relationships between soil balancing, home-grown feed quality and effects of these on dairy herd health.

Doug Spany knows downward spirals in market lamb and wool prices make it more difficult than ever "showing black with lamb. . . . I'm always preparing for the pasturing season we just had too," quips the city kid-turned hill country farmer who says, humbly, that he's still learning about feeding or breeding his 200 ewes and the 70 head of calves he's added to the operation. Mid-season 1992, he reported spring lambs are gaining, on average, five pounds ahead of the 1990 season. In that same span calcium levels expressed in plant tissue tests have risen 50% as a result of more and better cultured legumes in the pasture. Relative Feed Values (RFV's) have increased from a season average of 115 to 150. Doug says he may join a lamb marketing network which will bypass most middle profit takers.

Karl Stieglitz, asked two years ago why his milking herd wasn't out on rotationally grazed pasture like his heifers, scratched his head and said: "Well I just haven't got it figured out yet. It's the logistics; it's moving them. The timing. Who is going where and when." Today, working through the Rodale Institute, Karl has a new grant from the same DATCP sustainable ag program that made this paragraph possible. He's demonstrating dairy farming with producing cows on rotated pasture. He's also demonstrating use, feed values, and ensiling of alternative forages including soybeans, legume/grass and legume/grain blends and sorghum/sudan combinations.

Ruth and Dick Zinnicker understand there are small, helpful changes even the timeless ways of their ancestral agriculture. They and son Mark had been uncomfortable after research suggested critical nitrogen and some potassium, both held in cows' urine, was leaching from composted manure piles. This composting had always been an elemental part of the German biodynamic way of saving and creating fertility. What to do? Dick engineered a way, "for less than $5,000," to capture and store barn gutter urine. He bought a vacuum tank and now spreads the urine on winter cover crops he's experimenting with: rye, oats and oil radish. Dick's thought is these nitrogen-uptaking crops will gobble and store the volatile nutrient in roots and tops of the plants during die-back. "Our compost piles will dry faster, decompose quicker and spread easier too," Dick believes.

Mike Irwin
Lodi, Wisconsin,
July, 1992

Table of Contents

Dairyman Rick Adamski, 35, grew up on the 250 cropped and timbered acres he farms today, nine miles north of Seymour, in Shawano County. His Uncle Frank, father, Richard, and his mother, Evelyn, have spent their lives there too. So did grandfather Stanley, who bought in around 1900. Rick and three sisters, Carol, Jean and Mary, helped during their school years. After college, after three years managing a sewage-sludge-to-farms program for the City of Beloit, after completing graduate coursework in land resource management, then came a turning point...and a turning home for Rick.

Today he tends 40 cows, averaging 15,800 pounds of milk annually. He is active in rural development work, teaches and continues refining the rotational grazing system he began with his herd in 1987. The master's paper, with recommendations for the future of Maple Grove township, is alive but waiting. There is always something to do on the farm.

Grasses, grasses, grasses.
You need grasses in the vegetative state,
not the reproductive state.
Cows love them better than legumes.
Pasturing, you gotta have grasses.

— Rick Adamski

ALWAYS HAVE HAD A STRONG CONNEC-
tion with the farm. It's one of those things
you can't understand. It's a sense of belong-
ing. There were reservations about coming
home to farm. You know what goes
through your mind...it's too much work...nobody else is farming these days. And it was true. I went to school to meet
the alter-ego that says, "You can't do it." But I knew if I got
the chance, I'd come home....

My uncle was having leg problems, my sister was
disenchanted and my Dad was in his early 60's. I was at a
decision point. I've felt comfortable ever since, though there
are times you rethink....

We grow barley, corn and hay. Grazing was always part
of our pattern. I thought I could improve on that. When I
read what was happening in New Zealand with rotational
grazing, it was exciting, inspiring. I went to Walthill,
Nebraska, to see a small farms research project. I was impress-
ed. I talked with Russ O'Harrow, a dairyman at Oconto Falls,
who had been to New Zealand. With that inspiration I went
ahead and purchased the fencing material in '87. Then I applied for a grant. I was convinced this fencing and grazing
was workable....

It's single strand, with reels and plastic stakes. The perimeter fence was pretty much there from my father. I think I spent $1,000 for everything that first year, including energizers — the chargers. I've made more improvements, like on the perimeter fence, since then, with another $1,000.

The beginning of the grazing season is really critical. That first month of handling may predict how well the pasture produces the rest of the season. In the summer of '88 I changed the [portable] fence every day for the milking cows. In '89 I changed it twice a day in May and June. By doing it more often, giving them more pieces, they did a better job of grazing, keeping those grass seed heads trimmed.

Balancing rations was a big trick. I did lots of forage testing. I keep experimenting. Baling hay, we do make about 4,000 bales a year. I give the cows about five pounds a day, even while they're on pasture — a little at each milking.

Worms, I do no different than before the grazing project started. Bloat was a problem for me in '88. I lost a 13-month-old heifer. She showed me some signs. I was a little alert but didn't realize how serious it was. There's a product that's been really effective for me since. It's poloxalene, a dry powder. I put one tablespoon in the grain per cow, per milking, per day.

Now this is an interesting story — what I did to alleviate the bloat problem in the pasture, especially late summer, early fall. That's the bloat time — heavy dews and a lot of rainfall...with a lot of lush growth. I don't put the cows out on the alfalfa-grass pasture overnight. They're out there during the day when there is no dew. And when the barley is taken off — the first year there's no new seeding, just straight barley — I run through it with a quackdigger and then stimulate the second crop regrowth. That becomes my night pasture for the cattle. You go to bed not having to worry who's going to be bloated in the morning. They don't bloat. There is a chemical reason for it but I don't know....

You'd be surprised to find out the barley, six inches to a foot tall, is 25 percent protein, about 20 ADF, and right around 40, NDF. Uncle Frank had always grazed the regrowth of oats and barley, but I'd never taken a forage sample. If the cows had free choice, both fields open and equi-distant, they'd go to the barley before the alfalfa.

I remember going across the road as a young tyke to the milking barn — across where Grampa and Gramma and Uncle Frank lived. I'd go across with Dad. Grampa was fascinated by me; I think he liked kids. We would sit and talk; we had a neat relationship. He had wildlife and science books. We'd talk about 'em. So maybe that's where my inquisitiveness started. That and some good teachers I had in high school.

The teaching I have done for Northeast Wisconsin Technical College at Bonduel is fascinating. I was hesitant. Did I have the knowledge, energy and time? The ag dean there said it was important I do it; sustainable agriculture had a lot of interest.

Sustainable agriculture means more than rotational grazing. We need more farmers. This agriculture is one means of achieving that goal. Anything I can do to help someone stay in farming or get started farming I'll do. That's my goal in life. I've had people tell me you're crazy talking like that. They're making fun of you, but you're still on your way to the bank. They say: "Why do you share this; why not keep it to yourself?" But that doesn't fit my lifestyle, my philosophy. I can't go with the models we've been taught — if I beat my neighbor, it's for the common good? I can't understand that — me first, technology first.

Learning From My Field:
Starting Out With Rotational Grazing.

■ Start small, on a 20, with good, strong, perimeter fence.

■ Read as much as you can. Bill Murphy's *Greener Pastures on Your Side of the Fence,* for example, and subscribe to *Stockman and Grass Farmer.*

■ Visit with other farmers who have experimented or bought some of the materials.

■ It's good to keep grazing height about 12 inches. That way the cows don't tramp down too much and there's still good nutrition.

■ Constantly be alert so you can gather information about your cattle and the pasture from the moment you leave them out until the time you retire.

■ Grasses, grasses, grasses. You need grasses in there in the vegetative state, not the reproductive state. Cows love them better than legumes. If you're pasturing, you gotta have grasses.

Since 1980, Toni Christenson and her workmates have transformed a small landholding, once dominated by a baseball diamond, into a lush, lucrative, organic vegetable operation. The five acre, raised-bed commercial garden and its roadside sales center are located on Highway 57 near Sturgeon Bay in Door County. Besides May-to-October direct sales, Bright Eye Farm markets a variety of leafy and summer vegetables, blossoms, herbs and berries into area wholesale and retail stores, restaurants and supermarkets.

For Toni the gardening is part of a larger quest for balance. She is also a psychotherapist.

You had better love it
or not consider it –
even if you make a pile of money.
If you don't love it, Mother Nature
is always going to beat you up.
She's always there as trouble . . . .

— *Toni Christenson*

EN YEARS AGO WE COULDN'T GET A REST-
aurant salad in Door County that wasn't
made of head lettuce.
"Why is this?" we asked.
"It's hard to get variety lettuce."
"Well, we can grow that."

We started with lettuce and spinach. We were well
located for that. We saw no point to shipping in vegetables
from Texas or Florida or California when they are easily
grown in Wisconsin during the warm season.

We tilled the baseball diamond first. We picked stones
for the next two years and we spread raw materials while we
started building our compost piles. We were using horse
manure and bedding straw from a local stable. And sawdust,
chips, leaves and pine needles. Later we added refuse from
crops and sales leftovers from the markets to make the compost.... Within two years all piles were turned over and applied. For five years we worked, and nobody really noticed
what we were doing. We couldn't run off to see what others
were growing — not in summer. We were pretty isolated and
overwhelmed for awhile.

There was a lot of reading and research. The Rodale Institute helped us a lot. We subscribed to *Acres USA*. That

was an education! (laughs). I do think farming is political. I still go back to look at *Acres*.... We wanted to practice something other people could adopt and we wanted to show them how to do that. We started doing newspaper articles, columns. They helped. We started speaking to groups — Door County Environmental Council, women's clubs, backyard gardeners and small commercial growers. When people come to the store, we say: "Here's what you can do."

We grow three successions of crops. In the first we start in the greenhouse and transplant six varieties of lettuce. Spinach and pea pods we grow too. In the second, the summer crops, we grow tomatoes, peppers, eggplant, summer squash, winter squash, pumpkins. In the third we go back to the leafy vegetables again.

We are certified organic growers and label this way. We use natural weed and insect controls. We use cover crops like white clover and buckwheat for weed control along with hoeing. We use insecticidal soaps, and lots of BT — bacillus thuringensis bacteria — which kill many insect larvae. We companion-plant nasturtium and marigolds. They're pretty — and edible. We think they confuse and repel insects. We stagger bed plantings to confuse insects. We put a leaf crop, a root crop, an herb crop. We stay away from monoculture. Restaurants are buying the flower blossoms now for salads. They didn't at first.... Fertilizers — we work in cover crops and also use fish compost and foliar sprays.... We will spread three-four inches of compost within each two years.

It's fairly easy to do this if you care about what you eat and you care about the environment. There's really not a stray note in it. It all works together.... It is our respect for living systems.

Raising consciousness about the environment is hard — hard in our county, too, where main producers are dairy, feed crops, cherries and apples — operations that have always stuck with chemicals.... People, tourists, would come from Chicago. They would say: "We're allergic to this.... and this. We can't have anything but organic vegetables." From the pollution they lived in, these people knew.... People in our area are still coming in. The past two years there's been a change.... Our Piggly Wiggly grocery store — we're grateful to them. They're so open to our vegetables now. Of course they had clientele saying: "Why don't you have organic vegetables?" That's what has to happen....

The more I do counseling and farming the closer together it all comes...the less disruptive. Sometimes it is terrible. The beans are ready. We have a huge lettuce order to cut. Then you just do it.... If you love it, you just say: that's okay, that's the way it goes.

I will always do two things. I need the balance. We will get better. I know we can't be perfect. I don't ever want to go bigger. I don't like machines. I like things with few moving parts. Hoop hoes and garden carts are good. Keep it simple...and not very expensive.

Learning From My Field:
Producing Organic Vegetables for Market.

■ Watch initial capital outlay carefully. Start small, on one acre. Do a leaf crop or summer crop based on your markets. I'd start smaller if I could do things over.

■ Focus on soil building. This helps crops through stress times.

■ Have markets in mind before you produce. Look at valuable crops. Labor is intensive and expensive. Focus on markets and keep client contacts up on a regular basis.

■ Be aware that if you miss a single day in the field in season, it's not good.

■ Planning is important but be flexible within your plan. You must know what crops do well in your area and what markets are open to them.

■ Look for labor exchanges, barters, cooperative work ventures. This kind of work can also succeed for a family with access to labor and willingness to work hard.

■ Read people like Wendell Berry, Helen and Scott Nehring. Also read Eliot Coleman's book on organic gardening. They remind us we can't farm by hurting things in our surroundings.

Vince and Dawn Hundt, both 38, live high in the coulees in La Crosse County, four miles north of Coon Valley, on 280 acres. They harvest 60 percent of these acres in forest crops.

The year 1989 was a great season of changes for them. They sold their 40 dairy holsteins, and moved Jake, 10, and Julia, 7, to a private Waldorf school in Viroqua, modeled after the teachings of German educator, farmer and mystic Rudolph Steiner. While Dawn pursued outlets for her art and craft skills, Vince further developed his woodscraft and business ones. He refined and extended markets for tractor-mounted wood winches and portable on-farm wood and paper chipping-shredding tools. He next modified a John Deere hay baler to make shredded paper bales. His video, funded by a DATCP grant, shows woodlot owners how to regenerate native hardwoods and push tree harvest earnings to the limit.

It is a bitter late winter afternoon here. As Vince finishes spreading baled paper bedding for replacement heifers he raises and sells for cash, Dawn prepares a supper including a casserole made with shiitake mushrooms the family cultures on ironwood (slippery elm) logs. In their library a long shelf is filled with popular hardbacks on physics, astronomy and natural science. Vince's hands move and sweep, seeming to conduct the symphony of ideas that flows out of him.

**Work in the woods properly and
you can get the same-sized check
every year as the tobacco farmer
does on two acres.
You can do it forever.
It's a renewable resource . . . .**

— Vince Hundt

ELLING MACHINES AND FARMING THE woods came from the same source of inspiration. Have your mind open for opportunity! Look at your enterprise from every conceivable point of view...every conscientious way to come up with money to feed the babies.

Every farm is different. A bed and breakfast works on one, and selling pumpkins along the road on one. That don't work here. There are some days with a fresh snow there's no track on this road at noon. If you're not near a city, what do you have? You've got your personal abilities, your ideas....

Well, we had this farm of 280 acres. We were farming only 115 acres. What about the rest of it? We made a pie chart of our farm. Corn, oats, hay, pasture, farm buildings.... The woods — it was waaaaahhp — way out here! Most of the pie. Hey, come to think of it there *is* a crop growing out there. Same sun, same rain, same soil as the rest of the farm but nobody's weeding it, culling it or harvesting it.

Now say you're a western Wisconsin dairy farmer, milking 40 cows. The end of October comes. You've got choring that takes up two hours either end of the day. Four to five months of the year you're underemployed. Why not head for the woods the rest of the day? In these woods you've got valuable resources, possibilities. The commercial logger sees X quantity of valuable timber. He finds 25 good stems and to hell with the rest of it. A hard scrabble farmer sees everything as valuable. Forestry products are things with lots of value added right off the bat. Firewood's free laying in the woods. Buck it up, bring it to the road, it's $100 a cord. Take down mature trees, drag 'em out and sell 'em; they're worth more. Saw 'em into boards on your sawmill; they're worth more. Make a roll-top desk and sell it, you've got $2,000 a tree.

A hundred twenty-five years ago the first farmer, the second, the third took what he wanted from the woods — didn't give it a thought. We're now at the end of that cycle. We're in the midst of declining oak forests. And if we don't do something very ambitious and correct, it's going to be the end of oak forests. With this video we're trying to show how to do this whole thing, getting top earnings from the woods and regenerating valuable native species. We're doing it with a good attitude toward long-term economic and environmental consequences. Not only can you learn to farm the woods and write yourself a check every winter, but at the same time you can dramatically raise the value of your farm.

I go out every fall and select a spot. I mark it off.... like an acre and a half. We begin by clearing all the small stems, even if they're oaks. We just took 2000-3000 stems from an acre. Only three were oak. Everything else: box elder, soft maple, poplar, bitter hickory, basswood, rock maple — crap! There's no pulp mills near here. So after cutting small stems we use some herbicide — tshtt, tshtt like that — on the stumps and 1 to 2 inch sprouts. Now they won't come back.

Next we take the pole-sized wood. If they're the wrong species, we spray their stumps too. Otherwise we let the stumps sprout. Next we take out the firewood-sized pieces.

Most is ironwood. We use these for sprouting shiitake mushrooms. It's an amazing discovery — this worthless tree turns out to be best for growing shiitake spores. This sized wood we also run through our chipper. In some places chips bring $20 a ton. Around here, not much.

Now we're at the stand of big oaks. We knock those down, pull 'em out. The top goes to firewood, for shiitake logs and chips. We've opened everything up, clear cut it. Next spring the sun comes in, hits it, and those old stumps will sprout. In April we plant 1,000 trees in there. Red oaks, walnuts, white pine. We are doing what the burns, the forest fires, used to do — regenerate oak forest.

The problem with clear cutting, the aesthetic thing is hardest to accept. And the solution is not to do too much in any one place. I do one acre, two, three, scattered around our 180. The soreness on the eye is still in the eye of the beholder. I feel that acre is beautiful, more beautiful than any acre around it. You're putting something back....

This is maximum benefit to wildlife, I mean a gift to them. You make a varied eco-system out there. I've got forests one year old, four years old, seven years, ten years old. Different species like different stages. Our four-to-eight years cut was a bedroom community. Rabbit tracks, squirrel, partridge, fox, coyotes, deer. We always leave a perch for predators in the middle of a clear cut. In spring that cut's full of small warblers that like thick, low canopy. A hundred yards away you've got mature forest with turkeys scratching around. You've got cavities in old oaks for owls and woodpeckers. Small clear cuts are the best thing you can do for your woods.

Don't log and sell 25 acres at once. You move to a higher tax bracket. You mentally forget that woods for a generation! You don't develop a forestry mentality. It's forgotten, it's history. Money spent and lost. The way we do it, you're going to get $5,000 to 6,000 thousand a year forever.

Learning From My Field:

Farming the Woods.

■ Give yourself some education. Show initiative. Read a book or start with your local forester. Go out and look around. See what you have in your woods.

■ Develop an overall woods plan. Read woodlands association magazines. Look around again. It'll help you develop a woods consciousness.

■ Get some safety education on felling and cutting. If you wind up dead or broken to pieces, it's a failed project. Safety learning is the difference between driving drunk with the lights off and driving sober and rested, midday, down the right side of the road. Sure it's dangerous out there. But wear safe gear and follow simple rules. Then chances of getting hurt are slim. (It would be good to see our video on this.)

■ Provide for your safety with decent tools and equipment. Then give 'er hell.

■ The more you do yourself, the more value you add.

■ Use the woods. It can enhance your income and the value of your farm.

By day I teach journalism and technical reporting at Madison Area Technical College. By dawn and dusk, by weekend and summer I raise specialty crops for regional organic food markets. These include amaranth, soybeans, azuki beans, and hard spring or winter wheat and legume seeds. I live with Leigh, 48, who is a vocational counselor, and daughters Fritha, 9, and Autumn, 7, near Lodi, in Dane County.

***Cultivating specialty crops is
cultivation of a guerilla mind.***
— *Mike Irwin*

OST OF THOSE WHO HAVE TOLD ME
— and are now telling you — their stories
earn the biggest part of their livings from
the land. In that meaning, I am not a real
farmer. But my life in agriculture *is* real.
For me, agriculture has meant an odyssey of intellect and
spirit. It's been a revisiting of our first human frontier and an
emersion into the last and a most elemental one on Planet
Earth.

I'm a crofter — a small farmer — a dabbler. I've never
worked more than 60 acres in a season. I come part way to
farming by my grandparents' culture, crafts, habits and
blood. And maybe I come further by my love of open spaces,
my itch for learning in natural science and by a big batch of
simmering, raw energy somebody poured into me.

My parents weren't farmers but I worked on farms, including those of relatives and friends, from the time I was 12.
I picked strawberries. I cleaned gutters. I cased tobacco,
sweated gallons in haymows and learned to run machines.
During graduate school in the late '60's, I lived on a farm-
stead in a $50-a-month house not far from Sun Prairie, where
I mostly grew up. I had a dream then to someday own a small
farm.

What set me to experimenting with amaranth ten years
ago? I had stake in a small, stony, abandoned place on the
Baraboo bluff-top in Sauk County. I was putting in money
and working hard. So was my family. We saw only a little
profit. Corn, oats and hay for cash. Somewhere there I woke

up. I needed to stop competing with the big boys, the elevators and co-ops.

About this time I gave up using chemicals completely. Covering the environment beat for the *Capital Times* in Madison for the summer in the mid 1970's, I'd seen first hand what smokestacks and industrial chemicals did to fields and water supplies. Spot spraying corn had made me sick a couple of times and I'd had enough. Methods of organic farming began filtering into my reading. There was Balanger's *Countryside* and *New Farm* from Rodale.

The old timers raised in my hills changed my ways too. They would kid me at auctions:

"Farming in the bluffs? You'll never get closer to God than you are up there, but you're a long ways from the bank."

Or... "What you raisin'? Fifty bushel corn, fifty bushels a'rocks? That's about average. That's not corn ground, boy. Too cold. That's for hay and small grains if you got to work it..."

Then, in '80 or early '81, came a request from Rodale's *Organic Gardening* magazine. Readers around the country were invited to plant amaranth on small plots. Then after the season, we'd report what we observed to these botanists who had collected seeds from Mexico, Peru, Dahomey, Nigeria, Nepal. Those seeds, gathered for millennia, were traveling across time and culture and the life-spirits of many men and women. This dawning was a seminal, spiritual thing for me. I started experimenting, doing things only a handful of farmers were doing. From test plots to half an acre. Then to an acre. Then to ten.

I was asking lots of questions of older farmers who had threshed and cleaned small seed. Ray Palmer from Reedsburg helped me set up the combine the first time. Paul Pagel, my North Freedom neighbor, taught me, showed me how to clean and mill. He's still my master in this. And Wilfred Stone, near Sauk City, heard my drying and planting problems. He really put his engineer's mind to work for me. My father helped with thinking and design too. I'm lucky I had these great farmer-engineer minds to ease me along.... With their help, I've been supplying amaranth seed and flour to organic food markets ever since.

The Aztecs grew and ate amaranth and it wasn't only a staple, it was sacred to them. The Incas used it too. In India the Sanskrit word for amaranth, *randana*, translates to *sent by God*.

Amaranth is a high-protein, tiny seed, smaller than most clovers and larger than timothy. It's full of protein-building amino acids including lysine, as well as calcium, iron and vitamins. Cook or mill it into another common grain like wheat, oats or corn and you've got near-perfect plant protein for hot cereal, pancakes, bread or crackers. That's what laboratory people are saying. That's what I tell customers.

I think *amaranthus retroflexis* — common pigweed — must be native to Wisconsin. At least it's native to my fields. The amaranth we plant has been crossed or reselected from original Rodale seed gathered from Africa and Mexico, and is species-named *cruentis*. We do have to be careful retroflexis and cruentis don't cross when we're improving seed stock. Some worryworts say cultured amaranth will take over farm fields. Baloney. It's a sub-tropical plant and a poor competitor when cultivated or cut often as part of a crop rotation.

Today our rotation goes: amaranth, azuki or soybeans, hard spring or fall wheat nursing clover or alfalfa. I wish all farmers would give themselves an acre for play, experiment and failures. I thought and played for a long time on my whimsy-acre. I wanted two nitrogen-fixers in the commercial rotation which would also give me direct-market human food. Innoculated beans, that's one. And clover. You can bale it, combine it for seed to plant or sprout or plow it down for green manure. Maybe next I'll learn to row crop, pollinate and combine alfalfa. Get out of the way, Northrup King!

I find markets by working backwards *toward* the field and inside out from the product package. I start not as a farmer but as a shopper. I read ingredients and hunt the geographic sources of raw foods. Could I grow this? Maybe my acre for play will have another new bean or seed come to visit. I read up on the growing culture of my mystery crop. I know long distance suppliers and middlemen are vulnerable. They've got multiple markups and shipping and handling costs. There are many losers in their game. The local farmer, consumer and eco-system are some.

When I come from the field knowing I can plant a crop, cultivate it and combine it, I ask next: Can I get it dry, get it clean enough for human use? If so, I'll beat the britches off of my long-distance corporate competitors. I'll save the consumer, save energy, save myself. That's my thinking and my way. No multi-layered supply system. No Cargill, no Pillsbury will ever compete with local farmer guerrilla methods... or with a collective or producers' pool direct-selling organically produced or no-sprays food. Who, after all, would sing about such crazy things in a 30-second, 10 million dollar commercial?

Small is beautiful... and can be powerful.

Learning From My Field:
Growing Amaranth.

■ Tiny-seeded, slow-emerging as it is, amaranth wants a seed bed delicate enough to germinate a carrot. To give it such a nesting place, fall-plowed clover or alfalfa sods and / or light loams are the best way, but not the only way. Don't fall plow unless your plot is protected from wind and water erosion.

■ Plant amaranth with a walking or tractor-mounted vegetable planter at 24-38 inch spacing to match other farm tools and at ½ inch depth with one inch between plants in the row. Some plant using grain drills with some holes plugged. Others modify corn planters for dropping amaranth.

■ Amaranth has no pesticides registered for it. So technically it's illegal to use herbicides and insecticides on it. Don't worry about this now. You'll have other worries that are bigger and will come sooner.

■ Be ready to cultivate amaranth before or just after emergence during the first 10 days of June in the Upper Midwest. Here the crop starts slowly. Cultivate it like you would an emerging vegetable crop. A rear-mounted cultivator alone won't do. You must have gangs hung in front too. Three-to-four tractor cultivations are normal for amaranth producers. Lines we select in our region finish 4-6 feet tall.

■ After cultivations, but well before frost, consider a "walking bee" to catch small-seeded weed stragglers in your amaranth patch. Cut them low to the ground during their bud or green seed stage so they can't rise up again.

■ Be ready for harvest. Three-to-seven days after killing frost you'll be in the field. Set the combine up as you would for clover except keep header up to four feet, cylinder speed at 800 rpm or lower with ⅝ - ¾ inch clearance. Keep wind at or slightly above timothy gleaning settings.

■ Dry amaranth to 12-13% moisture on a barn floor or use another small seed method depending on your volume. To determine moisture with a digitized tester, use corn reading and drop two full points for amaranth. It's not perfect but close.

■ Except for your experiments and family use, don't grow this crop without a solid, written contract. Amaranth makes great hog or chicken feed, but it's a little expensive used that way. Be sure to investigate your contract buyer's background and business practices before you sign.

Bernie and Nancy Kleiber, both 40, have worked their own farm in Jefferson and Walworth Counties, three miles east of Whitewater, since 1973. With children Danny, 15, Peter, 11, and Katie, 8, to help out, they have cash-cropped corn and soybeans. Now winter wheat has been added to their rotations. Working alone at first and in recent years with the Michael Fields Agricultural Institute, out of East Troy, the Kleibers have done pioneering on-farm experiments with pesticide and fertilizer reduction, cover cropping and mechanical weed control for the past eight seasons.

It was my wife Nancy.
She was the motivating force.
She said: "Bernie, we've got to
get rid of these poisons."
— Bernie Kleiber

 ALWAYS WANTED TO FARM. INITIALLY I was sidetracked; I went to the seminary for awhile. But I always wanted to farm... instead of the job pressure things.... I was raised on one about 100 miles north and east. About halfway through high school I decided. I had one narrow focus, one driven thing, one goal in mind.

I studied agricultural economics at the University of Wisconsin-Madison to get experience in how to handle credit. I didn't have any knowledge of it... I guess nobody would at that age. But I figured it would be my major tool. If you want to own your own farm, this knowledge is critical. Learning about credit, I saw that people who worked their own land, who bought their own farms, were in a much better position later in their lives than people who rented all their lives. You've got just so much money. You rent land and you spend any extra on equipment. I wanted something more concrete than that. Owning land has intrinsic value in itself. I also farm because I like control. I worked for Production Credit. I worked in a factory at night. I don't want any more bosses.

You want to try new things. But you find you have to constantly monitor family life and the farming. Things seem always to tip toward more farming. Then you see the kids slipping away.... It brings you back in balance.

Looking at the economics of ridge planting, we saw how much better they were. We also were looking for a system that would control erosion on some of our land that was more sloping. We'd tried soil savers and the offset disk. We never had real good results — like on the poorly drained soils. Doing erosion control through ridge tilling convinced us too. We went in together on a cultivator with a neighbor. After a month I saw the economics of it. I said that's good enough for me. I bought the neighbor out. Now even if I wasn't ridging, I'd have a high-residue cultivator like a Buffalo. I wouldn't sell it. It's so advanced. If I went back to moldboard plowing, I wouldn't sell it.

Well, with the ridging system we were open to banding the herbicides. My wife hates to see us working with all this poison. She was the real motivating force to pursue banding. She got me the *New Farm* magazine. She got me to go out and see Dick Thompson. One thing led to the next.... I got involved in kind of the grass roots — the first sustainable agriculture meeting in Stevens Point. Then I made contact with Michael Fields, a non-profit ag. institute. I was trying to get some of these chemicals out of my system at that time. The work with Michael Fields led us to Wisconsin DATCP demonstrations. We could make our findings in the field public knowledge that way.

I'm much more conscious in the use of pesticides than when we started.... We're even testing our well water this year. We're more aware of erosion. We're seeing a building up of organic matter in the soil. It had been falling for years. Now it's up a couple points.

The combination that works is the ridge planting in conjunction with banding herbicides and rotating. I wouldn't back out on them. We use a Hiniker planter and the Buffalo cultivator. Herbicides I cut back right away to a third of what I had used. I can hold the line there. When I went down to nothing, I got a slow buildup of weed pressure. Now we've narrowed the herbicide band to eight or six inches and make it hot enough to control weeds there from the beginning.

Nancy does the rotary hoeing, the first time about four days after planting. Then right after the plants are showing. Then the third time is kind of arbitrary. The first one is the one that counts. Then I do two cultivations. There's a lot of residue so the first time it's very deeply — about four inches — and throwing trash to the row middles. I come back a second time, cutting it shallow so I don't get into that newly-developed root area. The yields with ridging and banding — well, I was kind of disappointed. Last year we moldboard plowed a strip that hadn't been plowed in nine years. The corn yields on that strip were the same this year as with the ridging. Not any better, not any worse.

Then we'll rotate out, including a legume for a couple of years and stop any more weed cycles. What we're working on now: start off with soybeans the first crop. The soybeans supply nitrogen for the following wheat crop. In fall you take soybeans off and plant your winter wheat. Then (February or March) you frost seed, broadcast your legume just when the ground is honeycombed. We haven't found just the right legume yet, but maybe annual alfalfa or annual sweet clover. The annual supplies nitrogen for the next corn crop. We'd been trying to drop a cover or legume crop in about September 10, at leaf drydown, but it was too late.

When we started with Michael Fields, we said in five years we'd be out of chemicals. I've found in continuous row crops it's real hard to do that. We'll probably still rely on banding. So we're changing our philosophy to using a much smaller amount. I figure we saved about $30,000 a year just on the system switch to ridge till. Then another $10,000 a year on annual purchased inputs. Even more because we've cut back on fertilizers, nitrogen and starter by a third.

Learning From My Field:
Cutting Production Costs in a Corn-Beans Rotation.

■ Banding herbicides is a first step. It's logical and anybody can do it. Start with an eight inch band.

■ Band phosphorous and side-dress nitrogen in the furrow. Side-dress any extra N post-emerge. It can be 28 percent or anhydrous.

■ Even if you're not ridging, a good high-residue cultivator, like a Buffalo, is important. Buy the cultivator first. Then come back the next year and find the planter. Using this entire system, you take control of that heavy wheel traffic too.

■ Cultivate deep that first time. It mixes soil and trash and aerates for root growth. It leaves loose earth for ridge building at second pass.

■ Try putting wheat into the rotation with frost-seeded legumes to fix N and build soil structure. This creates weed competition as well.

■ You must try planting and building ridges on your contours. They give terrific erosion control.

Ken Raspotnik, 40, with Darlene, 38, Angela, 16, and Sara, 12, keep 250 purebred Polypay ewes on 100 acres they've owned since 1976, just two miles northwest of Ashland. In season there may be 400-500 lambs on the spread. They rent 40 more acres next door for pasture and 200 more down the road for haying. Ken has reassembled six or seven settlement-era log houses and built a pottery studio in the woodlot near the family home. This is itself built of squared and dovetailed logs sawed from nearby woods. Barn and other outbuildings too are of his making....

The sheep are doing it for us.
We take care of the sheep;
they seem to take care of us.
And there's still time to
experiment with things
that might not go . . . .
— *Ken Raspotnik*

 WAS RAISED FIRST ON A DAIRY FARM. MY dad had 86 cows. He died when I was three. We moved closer to town. On the smaller place we raised young stock. I met Darlene here in public school.

I got an art education at University of Wisconsin-Stout, a specialty in ceramics. I wanted to be a teacher. I didn't get a job. Didn't work at it too hard....

We were interested in homesteading, getting back to the land. We wanted to be squatting on something. My ma, she gave us 40 acres. I started out as a potter, built a pottery shop over there, got enough money to build a kiln. So I started selling out of there for awhile.

We had a few animals. Goats. We had a horse there. So we started looking at sheep...probably 13 years ago. We had ten animals that first winter, a few ewe lambs. Then 30 the next year and then 60 and 90....

Well, getting to the Polypays, we started out with other grades and crossbred ewes first. Then we bought a Finn ram from the Spooner experimental station. There's a Finn parent in the Polypays (a four-way cross of Dorset, Targhee, Rambouillet and Finn). I figured he'd give us the first multiple births. With more lambs the more earnings you'd get.

41

Then we saw a flock of Polypays for sale near Milwaukee. We went and got those...and kept building.... We've been with the Polypays I guess eight years. We've been earning our living with them the past three-four years. We take care of them; the sheep take care of us. All our lambs are born within one month in March and April, except for the stragglers. We could get bigger but we've got enough.

It's sane to be using less, as little as we can. Watch big business. They exploit wherever they go. I just got a bad taste for plastics and chemical companies who don't care where they are going. I want to make sure I know where I am going. I don't want to buy their drugs and chemicals. It seems more of a challenge to do things simpler but still enough to keep up with the times.

First I started farming with a horse. Just a horse. Then I found out there was no way I could keep up with the hay for the sheep. So I ended up buying tractors. I'm not a real purist. I'm half-way in between. I don't want to ever get in the fast lane of energy use. It's okay to be a little poor. It's a little more sane. I'm just renting here on the earth. I want to make it a little better here rather than worse.

With our project I wanted to get moving toward raising organic lambs. We are raising that way for the market and for the sake of the earth. People are getting more conscientious about what they eat. I mean to raise a product to meet those needs. I want to test lamb gains on forages ready at various times. Then rotate from one good crop at peak to another at peak.

We start out grazing about May 15, with comfrey in winter wheat. Comfrey is first out. They love it. Then winter wheat is taken. After that, the field is disked and we plant turnip seed and rape. Midsummer they get trefoil and grasses. Then comfrey and clover in a field nursed by oats you combined off. By late August the turnips and rape are ready.

We want to market a lean, lighter lamb off pasture, around 85 pounds, not the fat lamb marketers say they want now. It's crazy to market like that...with the producer fattening and the consumer wanting lean. We sell purebred ewe lambs ready to breed in late fall.

It's the sheep genetics I'm really interested in now. You breed a ram to your ewes. You can see progression faster with sheep than with cattle. It keeps farming interesting.

If I'm ever satisfied with what I've learned, I'd like to teach people who come here from developing countries...using our buildings...corresponding and keeping on learning. I'm a slow reader. I learn by looking at something and looking and looking...and then it's doing. Trial and error.

Learning From My Field:
Sheep-Lamb Handling on Rich, Rotated Pastures.

■ When our sheep first hit the turnips and rape, a few got full ears — swollen, full of water. We were watching and pulled them off to dry hay and put them back on later. Next time we'll let them in shorter periods at first.

■ The comfrey is 26 percent protein, and has quite a bit of water. Sheep won't be needing water on these pastures. It takes a greater body capacity and stomach to take in and make use of all the nutrients and water together.

■ So I won't put young lambs, under say 40-50 pounds, out in these without their mothers. The bigger lambs will do better on the rape, comfrey and turnips. The younger ones will do better on the more delicate leaves of trefoil, clover and alfalfa.

■ With clover and alfalfa you could have a tendency to have

bloats. You can have trouble. With fresh, rich pasture I'll put sheep on and take them off starting a couple hours at a time. In five-six days I'll say their systems will be adjusted.

■ Sheep won't get fat on these pastures. We're glad but the packer is not. We market lean, at 85-100 pounds. This is a heavy feeder price. You get 5-10 cents more for them than for full fat lambs going straight to slaughter.

■ So far we're finding out our pasture lambs will gain an average of .65 to 1.2 pounds per day on our turnips and turnips-rape pasture. The feedlot lambs do a little better, .70 to .75 pounds, but we figure a 40 cents per pound grain cost has to go into that too.

■ We don't have real worm problems on these pastures. The plants are fast growing and by rough tilling with a disk and reseeding another crop right away, we disturb the worms' cycles — their living place.

■ Get skeptical of all drugs. You can't test every one on the farm. We've learned some are damaging to life. Keep experimenting and you'll end up skeptical.

■ To get started in this, go with 30 ewes or less the first lambing and winter. Get to know them. Go slow and try different pasture crops. See what grows good in your area. Buy a little fencing. Make a little bit at a time. With sheep the initial investment doesn't have to be big.

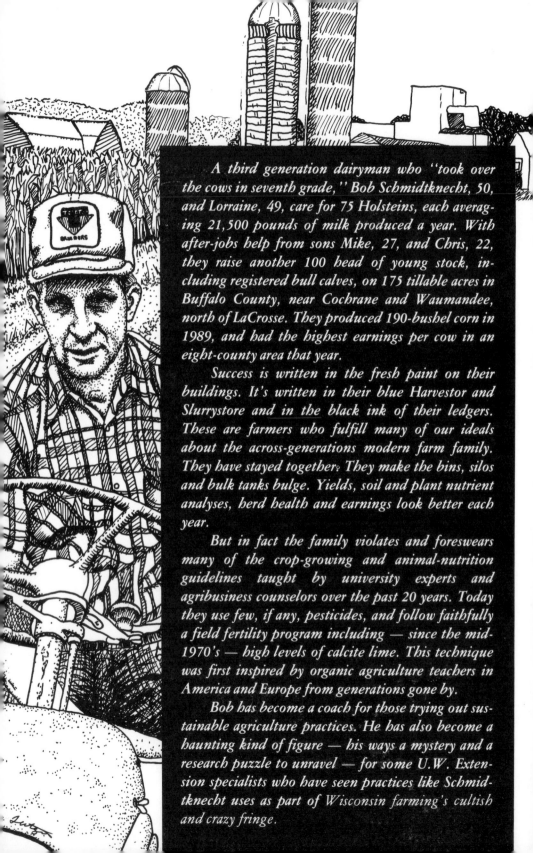

A third generation dairyman who "took over the cows in seventh grade," Bob Schmidtknecht, 50, and Lorraine, 49, care for 75 Holsteins, each averaging 21,500 pounds of milk produced a year. With after-jobs help from sons Mike, 27, and Chris, 22, they raise another 100 head of young stock, including registered bull calves, on 175 tillable acres in Buffalo County, near Cochrane and Waumandee, north of LaCrosse. They produced 190-bushel corn in 1989, and had the highest earnings per cow in an eight-county area that year.

Success is written in the fresh paint on their buildings. It's written in their blue Harvestor and Slurrystore and in the black ink of their ledgers. These are farmers who fulfill many of our ideals about the across-generations modern farm family. They have stayed together. They make the bins, silos and bulk tanks bulge. Yields, soil and plant nutrient analyses, herd health and earnings look better each year.

But in fact the family violates and foreswears many of the crop-growing and animal-nutrition guidelines taught by university experts and agribusiness counselors over the past 20 years. Today they use few, if any, pesticides, and follow faithfully a field fertility program including — since the mid-1970's — high levels of calcite lime. This technique was first inspired by organic agriculture teachers in America and Europe from generations gone by.

Bob has become a coach for those trying out sustainable agriculture practices. He has also become a haunting kind of figure — his ways a mystery and a research puzzle to unravel — for some U.W. Extension specialists who have seen practices like Schmidtknecht uses as part of Wisconsin farming's cultish and crazy fringe.

It's a lot of little things.
We put a whole system together.
We feed the soil, make it healthy.
That gives us healthy plants,
healthy animals, healthier people,
It all comes back to us . . . .

— *Bob Schmidtknecht*

 REALLY DO HAVE TO BE CAREFUL WHEN I talk about any of this…. Other farmers will think I've gone off the deep end…. My sister had just died of blood cancer the year before I applied for my sustainable ag grant. She was 38 and left three young kids…. There's challenges out there all the time. I'm one who thinks positive…. I figured, hey, if I can do something to show the agricultural industry how to change…. With my sister's cancer…. the time I'm putting in is worth it….

My dad, he was one of the first ones to use herbicide: 2-4-D, atrazine, insecticide too. There's still a lot of toxins in my soil, maybe more than in other people's…. I remember Dad mixing the stuff by hand in a barrel and doing custom work for other people. That was the late '40's-early '50's. He liked being first. We had the state plowing contest here in 1951. It was the forerunner of Farm Progress Days.

I'm one to try things out…. Really I started all this in the mid-1970's, using Nature's fertilizer. They recommended hi-cal [calcite] lime with it. So I was doing it, but I didn't know why then. I was getting the lime from across the [Mississippi] River in Minnesota. Extension started saying, ''Hey, you're wasting your money…. that much for so little fertilizer!'' But I was getting better and better yields.... Our slurry system came on then in 1976 too.... When I'd test high-moisture corn in fall, I'd be getting an extra percent-and-a-half protein and my trace elements would go higher.... That more than offset my expense.

Every year for the past seven we've spent less per acre on fertilizer and sprays.... In '88 we spot sprayed. In '89 we used none.... Our cows are producing more milk on 10-15 percent less feed.... My cost of production is as low as it has ever been. Herd health problems, well, I'm not there yet but it's coming.... We're down to 25 percent of the problems we had.... I say less leg injury and knee problems. Birth problems... well, now they push 'em right out. Our minerals are there now in our forages. You get the right nutrition, you see it happening: less cystic ovaries, less mastitis, less hoof problems.... Mastitis is a management thing....We have it. We don't have the hot cases we used to have....

Balance your soil and you'll balance animal nutrition and improve their health.... We do this following what Doc Rhems said, and I think what he said was true. You need calcium-magnesium ratios of five, six or seven-to-one in your soils. Calcite lime gets you toward that. I've tested dolemite lime from around here and found it 15 percent magnesium and 30 percent calcium. Well, that lime was in a 2-1 ratio. You keep sulfur levels up above what the University recommends; otherwise it takes more nitrogen to get your yields. Your phosphorus levels should be up above your potassium levels. Our phosphorus is high from the manure, but our potash (potassium) levels are still too high according to Doc Rhems. Our consultant is saying now we've got too-high potash releases in spring....

The University used to say you need this much potash to maintain. You know the good farmer.... We need 100 pounds, so let's give it 150. And that's what we did for many years. Of course manure helps keep our levels up too. I haven't applied any potash since the '70's except in slurry and a little in starter fertilizer....

We grow 70 acres of corn — about 25 acres for silage —

every year and 30 acres of oats or barley. The rest of the farm is alfalfa. We buy $70-80 varieties, not $170 varieties. We'll see how they hold up but I think they're going to.... We used to leave alfalfa fields three-to-four years. Now they look so good I don't know which ones to tear up. The corn goes two-to-six years on the same field. No problem. No rootworm or other insect problems the last two years. Not much alfalfa weevil either....

We apply liquid calcium and molasses, two gallons of each in 20 gallons of water per acre. We like to go with it right after planting the oats and corn — the same day or day after. The molasses helps feed soil bacteria. Your hi-cal lime goes on after first crop hay or some goes on after second. Generally I like to go with 500 pounds....

I'm seeing the whole program work.... Soil balancing has raised the sugar levels. The higher energy in that plant lowers the feed volume it takes for the animal.... I used the refractometer over the past five-six years.... Read the Brix levels which tell me sugar content. They used to read 5-to-6; now they're 12-to-13 and going higher....

An ASC guy came out last year. He said, "Bob, you've got some velvetleaf out there, but they're such scrubby devils, only a fourth as high as the corn...." Sure the weeds are still out there, but what if the [soil[environment is not out there for 'em?

Each weed is there to respond to or take a toxin from that field that's way out of balance. My dad started spraying in the '40's. He figured, gee, in two years he wouldn't have to cultivate any more.... There are more weeds now on most farms. Everybody admits that. Those weeds are telling us something. What do we do? Get out more spray. Kill 'em. Kill everything. Kill all bacteria in the soil....

Now we do need more nitrogen. More of all the fertilizers.... This is where the University's people are not looking.... I don't know about our Extension guys. I wish they could keep their minds open. It's sad....

Learning From My Field:
Starting Conversion to Soil-Balanced Biologic Farming.

■ Conversion time depends on how you do it. Maybe, if you'd jump away from the high magnesium dolemite lime, the anhydrous ammonia and the salt fertilizer. It might take three-to-five years and some yield reduction.

■ If you can manage it, get those weeds with a drag or rotary hoe and cultivator. Use disk hillers on later passes. It does take a little more time.

■ If you try this kind of weed control without getting rid of the anhydrous, the salt-fertilizers, the dolemite lime, and try going without pesticides, then you're going to get in some trouble.

■ Definitely soil test. Get a consultant working in the area of biologic or organic agriculture. The state soil test lab just tells you how to replace what you took off in a crop. It says nothing about balancing elements in the soil.

■ Balance that soil and you'll balance animal nutrition at the same time.

■ Take a little portion of the farm. Take a little at a time.

City-bred and raised, Doug Spany, 40, and Carol, 43, moved to a rough 200 acre, up-country spread four miles northeast of Wauzeka in Crawford County in 1986. She teaches half-time in a nearby school program for the gifted and talented. He travels and shears sheep in season. And with daughters Allison, 9, and Emily, 6, and their "rainbow coalition" of 150 ewes (Suffolks, Cordales, North Countries and Cheviots), they produce lambs and wool using intensive rotational grazing methods and fencing first developed in New Zealand. The fences are a combination of permanent borders with semi-permanent and movable "day fences" inside them. The inside fences are of light, portable, plastic, fiberglass and aluminum materials usually laid out in rectangles.

In a few years a few will
come around and say –
"He's pretty good at that . . ."
and my daughters
will appreciate
where they came from . . .
and it's the land . . . .

— *Doug Spany*

OMING FROM THE CITY, I USED TO HAVE the playground ethic. I still love to go and see the open spaces, the mountains. But going to see nature isn't going to save us; it may help kill us. I think we've all got to learn our sustenance comes from the land. We are landed animals, landed people.

...We've chosen this farm. We see all it is and grows. We'll never look at it like Allison and Emily do because it's their childhood.... I hope when they grow up — and I think Carol feels this way too — they'll keep this farm, or marry a neighboring farmer — or live so that they can understand where they came from, and it's from the land.

For me grass farming is really a way of dealing with the environment and our animals. I think when people get close to the earth, animals are part of their lives. Vegetarian diets are one way to get away from degrading the environment.... The trouble is most Americans aren't going to eat oatmeal or Wheaties all winter long....Growing vegetables takes a greater toll on the land than we do grassland farming....

Some of our land shouldn't even have a tractor on it.

The only flat spot on the farm is the living room floor — and *it's* not so flat.... Short of building stone walls, we couldn't have done without the New Zealand fencing technology. For us, everything inside the permanent perimeter fence is temporary. We're always looking for shortcuts to move the sheep every day.... We're getting some good stands of clover — 10 to 12 plants per foot in some pastures. Even with low lamb prices we're grossing as much as we would with 130 bushel corn at $2.30 a bushel....

We have a lot to learn. Really, we're getting some decent-looking sheep from one lambing to the next. We've got lean, marketable animals.... I'm troubled by the range between the best lambs and the worst, and have some concern over carcass quality. Once we're not increasing our flock, I can come back and be more selective about bloodlines. In 10 or 20 years I hope we have a good, quiet flock — about 300 ewes — and a really good grassland management plan.

We've been talking about some kind of urban-rural people connection, something that would give city people a chance to feel some ownership of land and means of production. Having on-farm contract marketing with urban customers does come up. It would be a natural outgrowth of that landed people connection. Most of us farm because we like to get our hands dirty and don't like wearing nice clothes. But custom marketing may become an economic necessity.

I've been thinking lately sustainable agriculture could become greed-driven. If that happens, we're going to replace one problem with another. Being sustainable has to mean ecologically sound....Even if I had to choose between the two — and was a financial failure because of it — I would still be leaving our grassland pastures for the next guy to work on.

Learning From My Field:
Starting Out in Sheep While Staying in Balance.

■ Start small and simple.

■ Know the sheep you buy. Take somebody with you if you don't know — somebody you trust. You can make mistakes at this stage.

■ After sheep, start thinking about fencing and equipment. Later plant and improve grass and clover pastures.

■ Keep your workload and financial investment in balance. This project shouldn't become a burden financially. We bought solid, cheaper animals and got a few more animals doing this. Then we started breeding what we wanted into them.

■ Don't bite off too much. If you do, you get discouraged or depressed. You could become one more family setting out to do what needs doing — then ending up moving back to town.

California schooled and Wisconsin dairy farm season-ed, Karl Stieglitz began traveling back to work summers on his mother's ancestral place when he was in junior high. That work continued every summer until Karl finished his animal science degree at the University of California-Davis in 1973, and came to farm with his uncle and brother. He took over the 413 acres, which includes some rented land, near Greenwood, in Clark County, in 1980.

Karl, 38, and Donna, 33, "raised five miles down the road," have two daughters — Laura, 6, and Amy, 4. A registered nurse, Donna works part-time — in 24 hour shifts — at St. Joseph's Hospital, Marshfield.

To those who have visited him or read about his thought and methods, Karl is one of the no-corn dairymen.

If the greatest herd average
or the greatest tonnage is
your goal, well then, mine
isn't the approach for you . . . .
— *Karl Stieglitz*

 HERE ARE TWO WAYS TO MAKE A PROFIT. Hold costs the same and produce more or lower costs. To me the latter is the way to go.

We concentrate on growing and pasturing forages because, to me, that's the easiest way to eliminate herbicides. The cow, being the ruminant she is, can turn forages into meat and milk. Trying to get such an animal to consume ever-greater amounts of corn doesn't make sense. Corn takes the greatest amounts of nitrogen fertilizer. It's the most likely crop in rotation to turn into soil erosion problems. And to me it's not a necessary part of a cow's ration, if you feed other grains.

When I was growing corn, I would end up harvesting every month from October to May. When I'd figure it all out, I'd have as much cash in a cornfield as I would need to buy my corn. I had that desire to eliminate chemicals. Still I wasn't sure I had all the techniques and machinery I needed to cultivate corn. "What are we gaining with all this capital investment?" I started asking. "With all this corn silage and harvesting equipment? Really. Isn't the cow designed to do that job?" I reached a point where I sold the corn harvesting equipment and bought some better haying tools…a baler, a tedder.

My long-range goal is to feed only what small grain I can raise as a nurse crop and rely on forage entirely. Right now I feed about 70-30 mixed hay to small grain. I like barley as small grain because, nutritionally, it feeds like cob corn. About two-thirds of that total hay ration is haylage and one-third is baled hay. I plan on eventually substituting about 35-40 percent small grain for the corn I still buy in the total milk cow ration.

For us it's oats, barley, winter rye. I like planting rye after I fall plow. I use it for winter cover. I like it in rotation for its flexibility. If we're short of moisture, I'll get extra forage out of the rye. If I need extra bedding, there's no better straw than rye makes. If I need green manure, I can plow it down in spring.

After rye, I follow with forage sorghum. This gives me a good silage yield per acre. Then I'll follow with another small grain, barley...or oats. Barley is higher in energy but lower in protein than oats. It's less competitive with oats in new seeding. I feel good with either crop. With the small grain nurse crop, I plant about three-to-one alfalfa and red clover and include a forage grass like timothy or brome. The rate in pounds would be nine-three-two, or four-to-five, if brome

I like mixed hay stands for risk insurance. A crop failure will never be total with mixed stands. I like drying windrows with grass. They're just easier....Hay is easier to deal with if mixed. Sure, alfalfa is high in calcium and phosphorus. That's good for a milking herd but not so necessary for dry cows. We'll keep stands about three years. I'm not concerned with stretching them further. I'm interested in turning back that organic matter and getting nitrogen for the next crop of barley or sorghum.

We're rotational grazing our young stock. We find they're gaining two pounds a day May to October on stands of mixed hay. I hope eventually I can learn to maintain these pastures forever. The grazing has saved greatly in labor and handling time and costs. I'd like to get the milking herd out there too. I haven't got the logistics worked out....

There's a danger in going after perfection in any of our farming when we're already producing so much....We produce 16,500 pounds of milk, four-to-five tons of hay and 60 bushel oats and barley and five-to-six tons sorghum-sudan. I'm satisfied with that. Now, as long as we're outproducing ourselves year after year...then I'm thinking about protecting our resource base...making sure there's something available to future generations.

Before I started all this, I'd got to feeling there was a pressure on us — that this year a certain level of production was good but next year it's not good enough to survive. You're on a treadmill with that pressure from agribusiness, the university and society. You're never encouraged to reach a point you say, " I'm done. I'm happy with what I've accomplished. I'm where I want to be." This way I can limit resources I buy off the farm. Hopefully I'll be in harmony with Mother Nature — which, to me, is what it's all about in the first place....I want to build soil, watch environmentally safe projects change and develop. If I can't do this, I might as well punch a time clock....

Learning From My Field:
Asking Yourself About Your Farm's Resources.

■ Stop and look at outside resources. Are these necessary? Ask what effect using them will have on generations to come.

■ If you have livestock, ask how you can use manure over the whole farm and take proper credit for it...not just those acres close to the barn. To cover all your land with manure takes time. It's worth it for the long-term health of the soil.

■ If alfalfa is the queen, then recognize you might be having some problems with her. Why put all your hopes in a monoculture? You might get along better with a mixture.

■ Is it desirable to grow things really not so adaptable to your farm? For instance, alfalfa has problems in our heavy clays. Why shouldn't we be looking at promising clovers?

■ Many say we don't get good new hay stands if we use a nurse crop of small grain. I say we should look at using nurses with short straw and shoot for 50 bushels, not 100. Back off on nitrogen too, and we'll get good nursed hay stands.

■ You should know that low-input agriculture doesn't mean a low input of labor. Often the opposite is true. Motivation to turn a dairy operation toward sustainable practices has to come from within. The system doesn't pay you, but there's a payoff in the long run.

■ If the greatest herd average or greatest tonnage per acre is your goal, mine isn't the approach for you.

■ Don't try to do everything that's new to you at once.

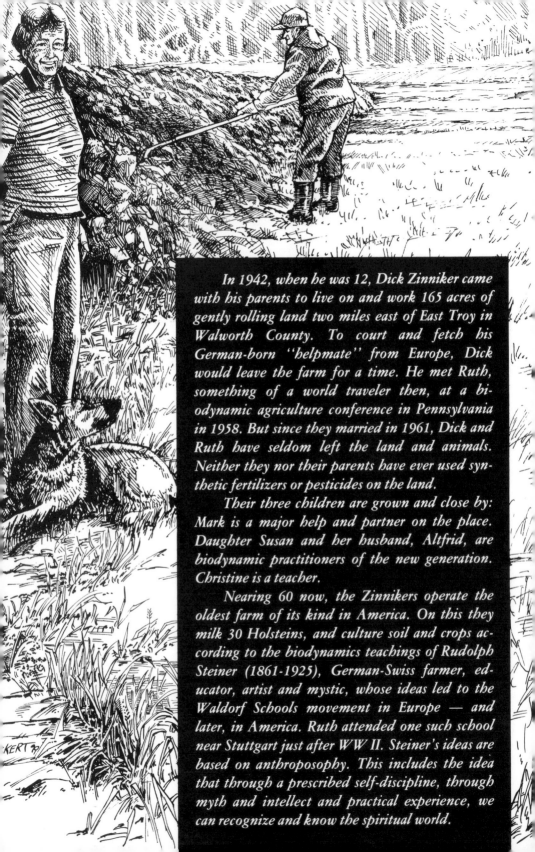

In 1942, when he was 12, Dick Zinniker came with his parents to live on and work 165 acres of gently rolling land two miles east of East Troy in Walworth County. To court and fetch his German-born "helpmate" from Europe, Dick would leave the farm for a time. He met Ruth, something of a world traveler then, at a bi-odynamic agriculture conference in Pennsylvania in 1958. But since they married in 1961, Dick and Ruth have seldom left the land and animals. Neither they nor their parents have ever used synthetic fertilizers or pesticides on the land.

Their three children are grown and close by: Mark is a major help and partner on the place. Daughter Susan and her husband, Altfrid, are biodynamic practitioners of the new generation. Christine is a teacher.

Nearing 60 now, the Zinnikers operate the oldest farm of its kind in America. On this they milk 30 Holsteins, and culture soil and crops according to the biodynamics teachings of Rudolph Steiner (1861-1925), German-Swiss farmer, educator, artist and mystic, whose ideas led to the Waldorf Schools movement in Europe — and later, in America. Ruth attended one such school near Stuttgart just after WW II. Steiner's ideas are based on anthroposophy. This includes the idea that through a prescribed self-discipline, through myth and intellect and practical experience, we can recognize and know the spiritual world.

*Agriculture is not only about
crops, markets and profits.
No, it is more.
It is about living
in harmony with the earth.*

— *Ruth Zinniker*

*We must disturb the environment
to grow crops and feed animals . . . .
We accept that.
Through our way, we disturb nature
as little as possible . . . .*

— *Dick Zinniker*

UTH: WE HAD A LARGE FARM IN SILESIA, in the east of Germany — what is part of Poland now. Villagers worked on the farm with 60 cows. Each herdsman took care of ten cows. There were 12 teams of oxen and 12 teams of horses. My father had studied agriculture at university. My mother was upper class — I wouldn't say blue-blood, but she had a governess. She had gone into nursing — homeopathic medicine. At home when I was a small child we had servants....

In about 1920 the chemical fertilizers were coming in. Educated farmers like my father asked [Rudolph] Steiner: Isn't there something we can do to avoid chemicals and still keep up with the times? Steiner was near the end of his life. On Whitsuntide, Pentecost, June, 1924, he had his assistants give the first biodynamic agriculture course. This teaching was not just from himself. His assistants had collected the ways, the stories from older people through many years. These tools were given to us, through Steiner, from nature.

We had to flee [the Russians] in '45. The Americans helped us.... We stepped across to the West side along with friends of my father   and sheep, cattle and horses. We got a farm the Nazis had been on. Father went to Stuttgart to the biodynamic research center. There was a Waldorf school there. I first went when I was 12. [Later] I did my two years apprenticeship and my year of farm schooling.... that was 1952.

My uncle invited me to America. I was his godchild and he would send me care packages. I came here...to New York...just to work...six months. I really hadn't wanted to come. My grandmother was here. She was reading a German-American newspaper: The Fetzers had a biodynamic guest farm in Pennsylvania. I went... stayed there one summer. Dr. Ehrenfried Pfeiffer was a student of Steiner. He was a German-Swiss soil scientist naturalized in America. He led meetings at biodynamic conferences near Fetzers' in the fall.

There I met Dick for the first time. I stopped here...at Dick's parents' farm in November. Didn't like anything.... My inside voice said then: "No, this is not my place. I want to work with my father in Germany." In two and a half years here I knew Dick only four weeks, but it was so strong.... We were such an odd couple. Nobody knew what we.... We didn't even get engaged before we got married.

My father passed away in '59. I said [to Dick]: "I go help my mother at home now." I came back here finally but I was torn apart for quite awhile. I wondered, what does destiny want from me? Why? It all seems right now....

To marry me he had to come to Germany. I felt he had never been away. Dick's parents had come from Switzerland.

His father was a commercial gardener in Chicago; he was interested in biodynamics. I wanted Dick to see the biodynamic farms. I had been to England, New York, California, Massachusetts.... I had been a servant.... I found out how poor the rich were and how rich I was...how they had everything... and nothing.

I grew up with biodynamics but explaining it is another thing. It is beyond organic agriculture.... it is adding more to the soil life. These things go into the compost pile...yarrow, camomile. They help the plant reach further for what it needs...the calcium, the potassium. You innoculate the compost piles and spread on the fields. We have two sprays. One is called 500; one is 501. They are used with old practices and ways that would seem funny to some farmers. But they are used in harmony with natural forces...one spray we use at germination...one at flowering.

We plant by the zodiac, the *Farmer's Almanac* basically. There are not many insects. I have a stinging nettle spray when insects come. You spray at night when leaves take it in. Or some you may spray with the rising sun.... The timing of the sprays is critical. It is in Steiner's course but it is also up to you. You can be clumsy. You can play.... This is open....A farmer must be a researcher as well as a steward of the soil.... There are forces we cannot explain but we can see they are there. Whatever language you would use for them does not matter....

DICK: In the '40's people we knew had seen biodynamic farms in Europe. I was 12 when we came here.... It all made sense — so father said. It was a different approach than the modern idea, you know: that if you get a lot of bushels this year, it's got to be good for everything and everybody. We didn't agree with that.

Starting out we were told: "You won't be in business ten years from now. You're not keeping up with technology...advancing...going with it." That was 40 years ago.... The funny thing is we haven't done anything different, just tried to improve what we did. Now people are saying: "Gee, you're something special," or "Hey, let's go see that guy." I haven't done anything....

It was hard those first years. The scientists from the farming conferences we went to in Pennsylvania would say: "Well, I've got to be there to help you." But, you see, there was no traveling to check out our problems. In America it was a poor movement. In the '40's organics and biodynamics were ignored. In the '60's the farm papers were still negative.... Now there's the organic movement, with the little guys hanging on — farming as a way of life. And the high-tech movement that says you've got to make your farm a business.

There is a lot of pain in farming. You really have to like it. There's so little margin in the crops. I produce 330,000 pounds of milk. There's not a lot of cash. I'd like a few machines.... I don't even know if I can say to my son Mark: "Do it! Go to it!" Or if the times are....

Sometimes I really think government is trying to eliminate small farms.

In the '60's people would come: "Oh, it's so beautiful outside. Yes, farms are wonderful." Four weeks later: "Well I didn't know it was like this...all this work."

You don't really get to watch the sunset. You're milking. It's always different once you get there than in your dreams.

I still feel satisfied. I did it the way I wanted to — not the best way maybe — but the best for me. I would do it again. I like the country. Being alone. I like the cows, not the steers. Cows stay with us for years.... You get a real nice personality; it makes you feel good. Mark likes the machines and crops. I've ridden old tractors with one-spring seats and two bottom plows a little too much....

Part of it is having a woman, a helpmate, to make it a pleasure. You're discouraged; she says, "C'mon, you know it will be all right." Having a woman with her background, I would do it all again. An' I bet not more than 20 percent of the people will say I like my job. My job has been to prove, in the great scheme of things — for 40 or 45 years anyway — that it can be done.... It can be done.

Learning From Our Field:
Experimenting With a Biodynamic Rotation.

■ We have a five-year rotation: Corn-oats-corn-oats-several seasons of hay. We start by plowing out of hay into corn.

■ We use heavy spreading of composted manure into the corn both times. We cultivate corn an average of three times. We have some weeds, but no one weed dominates.

■ We used to plant oats alone after first year corn. Now we're looking for another legume to go with it. This will give us a little more nitrogen. We're looking now at clovers...more clovers in the interseeding, more in the hay.

■ One of our favorites now is to follow oats with rye. Then use it for a plowdown...or maybe combine a little the next year. We've tried interseeding hairy vetch with oats and after oats, even into corn at last cultivation. We think the season is too short for vetch to help us in the first year this far north.

■ Third year is corn again but after it comes oats seeded with alfalfa, clover and timothy. We'll go two-to-four years with that hay field. But we've gone as long as eight. We like to give the hay a chance. Sometimes a field will be weak the first year and strong the next.

■ It's possible we'll be shortening our rotations. In good years we'll get 75-80 bushels of oats per acre and 100-120 bushels of corn. We're still experimenting.

■ Go slow, our parents always said, and keep trying new things out. To get away from chemicals and manufactured fertilizers, start out by getting into a legume. Try three acres this year and six acres next year. Seeing the good from these changes may take five years, maybe more.

■ The changes you'll see mean more than bushels or consumers paying premium prices for organic products. Much more. It's a way of life for the farmer and a way of the spirit too.

■ To read and learn more about the ways of biodynamic agriculture, write:

**The Biodynamic Farming
and Gardening Association
P.O. Box 550
Kimberton, PA 19442**